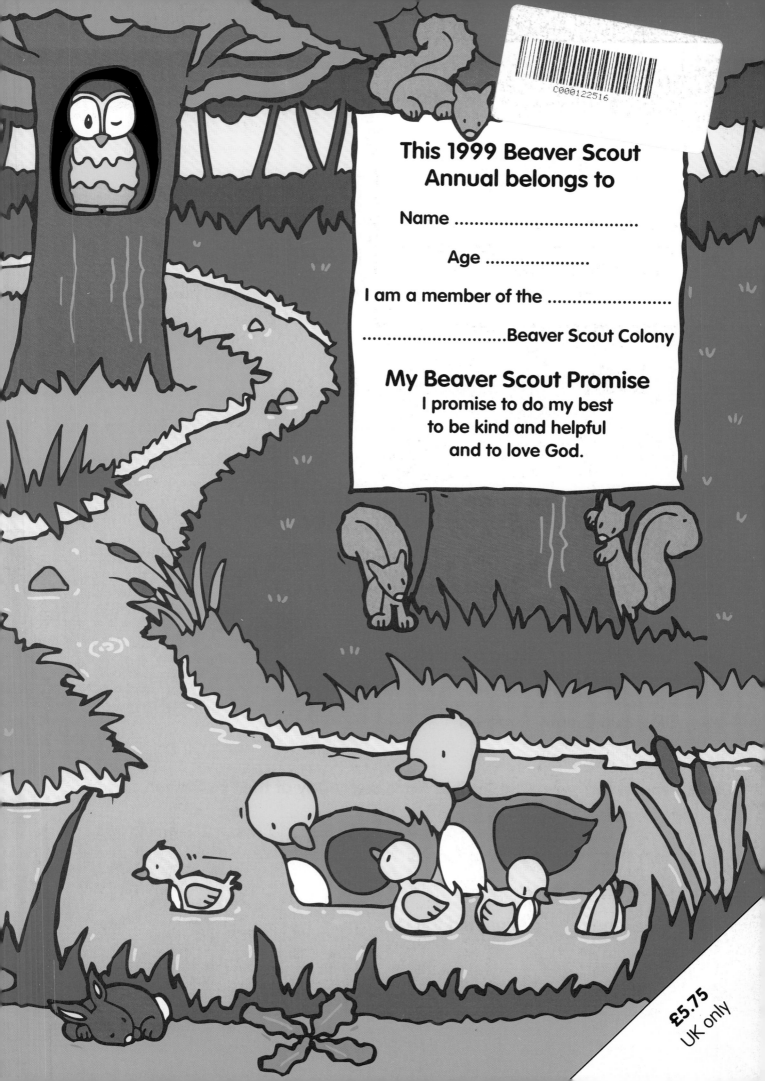

This 1999 Beaver Scout Annual belongs to

Name ....

Age ....

I am a member of the ....

.............................Beaver Scout Colony

My Beaver Scout Promise
I promise to do my best
to be kind and helpful
and to love God.

£5.75
UK only

C000122516

Contents

Safety Notice
Please note that some activities require adult help and supervision.

Billy the Sheep in
Arty Crafty Billy

1 Billy the sheep was the sort of sheep who liked to laze around in the long grass all day. He liked watching his friends, the lambs, bounce around the field.

2 He dreamed dreams of lying in a deckchair, on a tropical island, having all sorts of grassy treats brought to him by sheepdogs dressed as waiters.

3 Today, however, wasn't going to be a day for lazing around. Today was the day of the village fair, which Farmer Lott had said could be held in Billy's field.

4 As soon as Eggless, the cockerel, announced that it was morning – cock-a-doodle-doo – the field came alive with the sound of people in tractors arriving to set things up.

5 All the animals in the field went scurrying to the edges and watched the villagers set up the tents, sideshows and a big display arena.

Illustrations: John Shackell

Text: Dave Wood

6 Billy the sheep trotted off to the farmhouse. He met Farmer Lott's son, Ivor, who was walking towards the tent with a big cardboard box.

7 "Look, Billy," he said. "I'm going to enter one of the competitions at the fair." He showed Billy the model farmhouse he had made from sticks.

8 Billy was most impressed with Ivor's handiwork, and trotted over with him to the tent where the model-making competition was going to be judged.

9 But as they walked by a tent, Ivor tripped over a guy rope that was holding the tent up. His model flew into the air and landed, **crash!** on the ground.

10 "My model's ruined!" said Ivor. "It took me ages to make!" "Baaaa," said Billy, trying to cheer him up. And then Billy had an idea!

11 Billy trotted off and told the animals what had happened. They liked Ivor because he was kind to them, so they listened to Billy's plan.

12 The animals scurried away and Billy went to pick up the box, and Ivor's model. It had been dumped in a rubbish bin by Ivor, who was very upset.

13 Billy dragged it to the corner of the field and emptied the box. "Baaaa!" he called, and his friends came back with a collection of bits and pieces.

14 The mice had collected lots of tiny stones and the sparrows came with their beaks full of long, thin grass. The squirrels had bundles of twigs.

15 Billy told them how to build models. He wasn't an expert but he'd seen children build dens in the woods, so he had a few ideas of what to do.

16 The mice used the pebbles as bricks, and mud as mortar, and built tiny brick walls. The roof was made from flat pieces of bark, collected by the frogs.

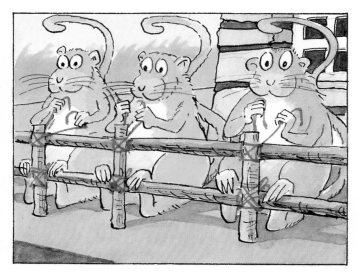

17 The squirrels nibbled the twigs to make them smooth and all the same length and the mice used the grass to tie the twigs together to make fences.

18 With soft feathers from the ducks, cloth was sewn into duvets by the hedgehogs, using spare spines as needles. These went on tiny beds made by the moles.

19 At last the model was finished! Billy put it in the box, dragged it over to the tent, lifted it on to a table and put Ivor's name next to it.

20 The judges were amazed by the model, and awarded Ivor first prize. Even though he said he hadn't made it, nobody else claimed it, so he kept the trophy.

21 "Thank you, Billy," he grinned, as he noticed his sheepy chum outside the tent. "I'm sure you had something to do with this, didn't you?"

22 Billy just smiled, and went off to see if there was a competition for lazing around in the sun and munching grass. He might just win first prize!

CHOMP! MUNCH!

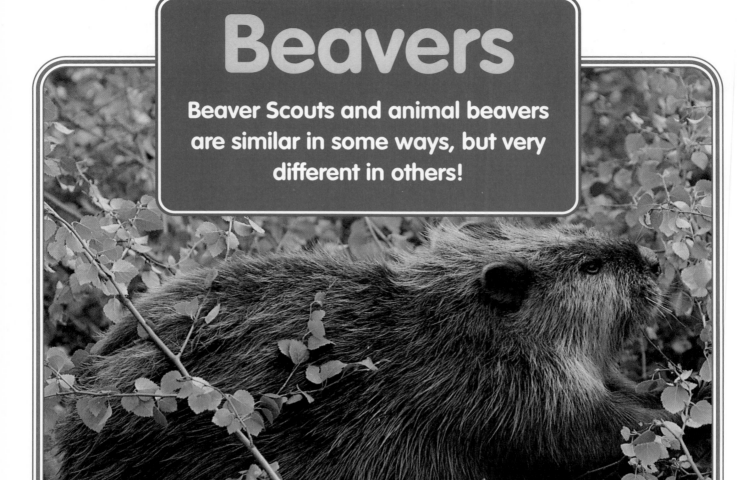

Beavers

Beaver Scouts and animal beavers are similar in some ways, but very different in others!

❖ There are big beaver animals and small ones, just as there are big Beaver Scouts and smaller ones. The beaver animal weighs about 30 kilos. How much do you weigh? About the same?

❖ The beaver animal measures about 120 centimetres from nose to tail. How tall are you? About the same as a beaver?

❖ How many fingers do you have on each hand, including your thumb? The beaver has five, too! He uses his front paws in the same way that you use your hands, to hold and grip things. The beaver is very good at building things with his hands. Are you?

❖ The beaver is a brilliant swimmer. His strong back feet have webs between the toes, to help him swim. Can you swim? Lots of Beaver Scouts can!

❖ How many teeth do you have? The beaver only has four! They are very sharp, bright orange, and never stop growing.

❖ The beaver has a large, flat tail covered in scales. He uses it as a rudder to help him steer when he swims, and to help him balance when he stands up. He also uses his tail to tell other beavers if there is danger by slapping it hard against the water.

❖ Beavers live mostly in North America and in parts of Europe and Asia. There are Beaver Scouts all over the world!

❖ Beavers are very clever builders and engineers. They cut down trees with their sharp teeth, and use them to build dams across rivers, making ponds. They use their flat tails like trowels, covering the dam with mud so water can't escape.

❖ Do you live in a flat or a house? I bet you didn't build it! The beaver builds his own home using logs and mud. It floats on the water, and has underwater entrances. It is called a lodge.

❖ Baby beavers are called kits. They are born in May and, just like human babies, they cry when they are hungry. By the time they are one month old they can swim well. Kits love to play, just like you.

❖ What do you like to eat? Write the names of foods you like, and compare them to what beavers eat.

my food	beaver food
	leaves
	bark
	roots
	young wood
	water lilies
	fruit
	flowers

❖ Where do you keep food in your house? In cupboards or the fridge? At the end of the summer beavers collect bark and leaves and put it on to a raft of wood. They sink the raft to the bottom of the lake and use it as a store in the winter, diving down for food when they need it.

❖ Beavers have two coats of fur. The one next to the skin is soft and silky. The outer coat is much thicker, and waterproof, which means beavers never feel cold. How do you keep warm?

❖ Beavers are friendly animals. When two meet, they make chattering noises, and rub their cheeks together. Are you friendly? The Beaver Scout Motto is Fun and Friends. It's a good motto for beaver animals, too, because they have fun and enjoy making friends. Just like you!

Draw a beaver. It's easy! Just copy this one.

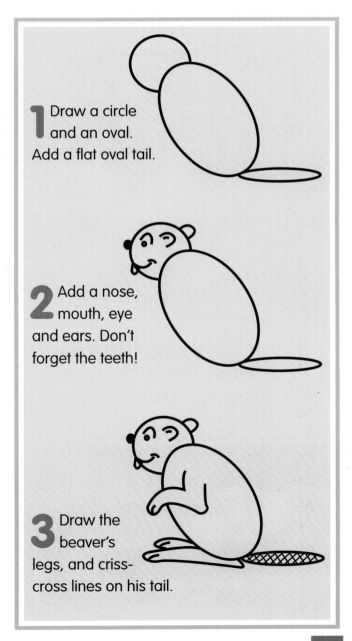

1 Draw a circle and an oval. Add a flat oval tail.

2 Add a nose, mouth, eye and ears. Don't forget the teeth!

3 Draw the beaver's legs, and criss-cross lines on his tail.

Hounslow Urban Farm

Let's join some Beaver Scouts on a visit to a very special farm where they met lots of animals.

An urban farm is a very special place. It brings a bit of the countryside into our busy towns and cities. It lets us meet farm animals without having to travel far way, which is difficult for some people.

A group of Beaver Scouts from the 1st and 4th Hanworth Beaver Scout Colony in London went on a visit to Hounslow Urban Farm. As well as being a city farm, it is also a rare breeds farm, which means that it looks after and breeds some kinds of farm animals that are endangered (in danger of dying out). It helps make sure that breeds like Hebridean Sheep and British White Cows will not become extinct.

The first animals the Beavers meet are rabbits. This is Tiny, a huge lop-eared rabbit.

Next – horses. Before tractors were invented, horses were used to pull ploughs.

Text and photographs: Alison Davis

12

The Beavers look in
the chicken coops...

...and find a freshly-laid hen's egg. Johnny looks after it until it is put into an incubator, a warm place that will keep it at the right temperature until it hatches in about 21 days.

This sow (the name for a female pig) is staying indoors because she has just become a mum. Can you see her spotty little piglet curled up beside her?

Pigs like rolling around in mud
– and having a good scratch!

Lots of ducks and geese live on the farm. This lake was dug out, and filled with water using fire engine hoses from the fire station next door.

Most goats are very friendly. This one is a pygmy goat, which means that it won't grow very big.

Billy goats (male goats) are not so friendly. This one is protecting his family. He keeps butting the fence with his big horns to warn the Beavers not to come too close.

A baby goat is called a kid. This one is just four days old.

These lambs (baby sheep) were born a few days ago.

"Can we take him home with us?"

Some animals have to be looked after if their mothers are ill or die. These orphan lambs are cared for by people who work at the farm.

This British White cow seems to like having her picture taken...

...and so does the calf!

Highland cattle live outside all year because they have long, thick coats to keep them warm.

BULL KEEP OUT

"I don't think we should go in this field, do you?"

What a Lot of Choc!

Yummy treats to make – all choc-full of chocolate!

Before you begin...
- Wash your hands.
- Put on an apron.
- Ask an adult to help you.
- Collect all the things you need.

Choccy Fridge Cake

You will need
- 225g milk chocolate
- 125g butter
- 2 tablespoons golden syrup
- 2 handsful raisins
- small packet digestive biscuits

1

Ask a grown-up to melt the chocolate, butter and syrup in a bowl over a pan of hot water. Remove from heat.

2

Crush the biscuits into crumbs. The easiest way is to put them in a plastic bag and hit them with a rolling pin!

3

Put the crumbs into a mixing bowl. Stir in the raisins.

Text: Karen Hankey   Illustrations: Wendy Hesse

16

4 Add the chocolate mixture and stir everything together.

5 Grease a baking tray. Press the mixture into the tray, using the back of a large spoon.

6 Put the tray in the fridge for about 4 hours. Ask a grown up to cut the cake into squares ... then eat!

Yummy Choc Sauce
(for ice cream)

You will need:
125g Toblerone chocolate
75ml double cream

1 Break the chocolate into pieces. Ask an adult to melt it in a bowl over a pan of hot water. Cool.
2 Stir in the cream, and pour over ice cream. Yummy!

Jacob and the Washing Line Thief

Illustrations: Mike Turner

Text: Sara Peach

Jacob was a Beaver Scout. He loved going to Beavers, but the other big love of his life was football, especially his local team, the Valiants. It was Jacob's birthday soon, and he was hoping to get a new Valiants shirt as a present.

Sure enough, on his birthday Jacob's mum and dad gave him a brand new team shirt. He wore it all day, and at his party. By the end of the games and food, the new shirt was covered in bits of chocolate cake and splodges of ice cream, so Jacob's mum said she'd wash it for him so that it would be ready to wear again next morning. She hung it out on the clothes line to dry, then everyone went to bed.

The next morning Jacob looked out of the window to see his new shirt fluttering in the wind. But it wasn't there! He rushed downstairs to ask his mum if she'd brought it in, but she hadn't! He went outside to see if his shirt had fallen off the line and been blown into a flower bed or into the branches of a tree. Jacob searched and searched, but his new shirt was nowhere to be seen.

Trevor, who lived next door, popped his head over the hedge. "What's up?" he asked. He was a photographer on the local newspaper, and he liked to know what was going on.

Jacob told him about his missing shirt, and Trevor helped him look for it. But it was no use – the shirt was gone.

Then Trevor had an idea. "I'll take your photograph, Jacob," he said. "We'll do a little article in the paper. It might get your shirt back for you."

"Thanks, Trevor," said Jacob's mum. "It'll be a while before we can afford to buy another one."

Poor Jacob moped about until a couple of days later the local newspaper came through the door. Sure enough, there was a big picture of Jacob in his bedroom standing in front of his favourite football posters. The headline said:

Local boy has Valiants top snatched by washing line thief!

Underneath there was the story of Jacob's shirt. He hoped it might help to get it back.

Someone else was reading the local newspaper at the same time. It was the manager of the Valiants, Luke Reed. He felt very sorry for Jacob. Losing his shirt must have spoiled his birthday. He decided to do something about it, and picked up the telephone...

Jacob was doing his homework when his mum came into his bedroom. She looked very happy. "I've got some good news," she told Jacob. "Someone very important is coming to see you tomorrow."

"Has someone found my shirt?" asked Jacob.

"No, it's something better than that," said his mum. "But you'll just have to wait and see!"

The next day, a large car stopped outside Jacob's house. Out climbed Luke Reed! Jacob's eyes nearly popped out of his head! Luke gave Jacob a huge box. He could hardly move. He couldn't believe it! Luke Reed – in his living room! He wished the Beavers were here to see this!

Inside the box was a brand new Valiants strip, complete with boots and a ball that all the players had signed. And there was an even bigger surprise! "Will you be the mascot at our game this afternoon?" asked Mr Reed.

Jacob was so pleased and excited that he could hardly speak. His mum had to nudge him to reply. "Yes, please!" he said. The newspaper article had said that Jacob was a Beaver Scout, so Mr Reed had tickets for all his Beaver friends, and their Leader, too.

When Jacob led the Valiants out on to the pitch wearing his new strip, the crowd gave a huge cheer. Jacob felt very pleased and proud. He watched the match with his friends, and they all cheered and jumped up and down, especially at the end of the game, which the Valiants won by two goals to nil.

After the game Jacob and his friends met the players and collected lots of autographs. Then they all had a meal together.

For Jacob, the best part of the day was when the players sang, "For he's a jolly good fellow!" after he had thanked them for a wonderful day, and for showing that no one – not even the washing line thief – could beat the Valiants!

Life in the Rain Forest

In the hottest parts of the world there are very big areas of land covered in thick forest. Let's find out about some of the birds and animals that live there.

Trees are the most important part of a forest. Hot weather and lots of rain make them grow very quickly. They provide food, homes and safe places for animals and birds.

Parrots are noisy birds that live in the tree tops. They have very bright feathers. Their big beaks are called bills. They use them to crack open seeds and nuts to eat.

The **sloth** has very strong claws that help it hang from tree branches for long periods of time. It hardly moves, except when it climbs very slowly to find leaves to eat. The mother sloth carries her baby with her.

The **tapir** looks a bit like a pig. It is most active at night, when it comes out to feed on plants that grow on the forest floor. Tapirs are good swimmers and like to spend time in water.

Ants live on the floor of the forest. They eat leaves that drop from the trees. They can lift objects that weigh much more than they do. They carry leaves to very large nests under the ground.

Illustrations: Guy Parker-Rees

Text: Brenda Apsley

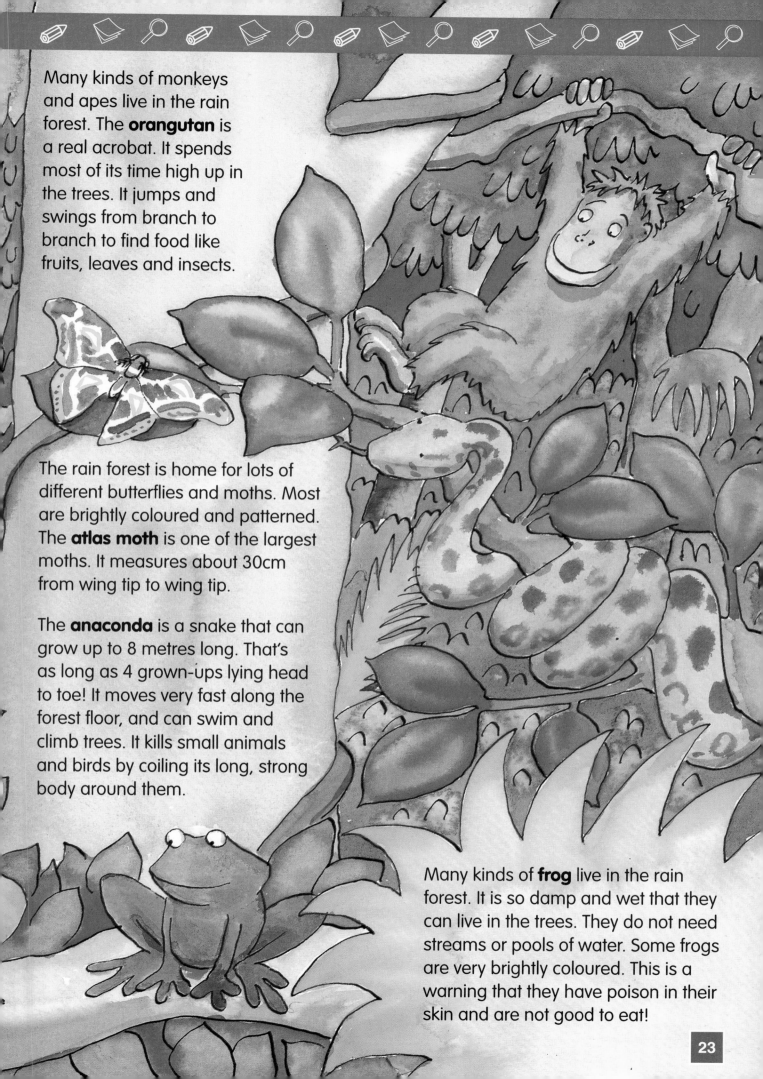

Many kinds of monkeys and apes live in the rain forest. The **orangutan** is a real acrobat. It spends most of its time high up in the trees. It jumps and swings from branch to branch to find food like fruits, leaves and insects.

The rain forest is home for lots of different butterflies and moths. Most are brightly coloured and patterned. The **atlas moth** is one of the largest moths. It measures about 30cm from wing tip to wing tip.

The **anaconda** is a snake that can grow up to 8 metres long. That's as long as 4 grown-ups lying head to toe! It moves very fast along the forest floor, and can swim and climb trees. It kills small animals and birds by coiling its long, strong body around them.

Many kinds of **frog** live in the rain forest. It is so damp and wet that they can live in the trees. They do not need streams or pools of water. Some frogs are very brightly coloured. This is a warning that they have poison in their skin and are not good to eat!

23

Build a Beaver Dam

Billy and Ben are beavers.
"I can build a dam faster than you!" says Ben.
"I can build one faster than you!" says Billy.
Who will be first to build a dam across the river, Billy or Ben?

Play the game to find out.
Play with a friend.
One of you is Ben.
The other is Billy.

Text: Brenda Apsley   Illustration: Jo Turner

Billy Beaver's Dam

You need a pencil, coin, and two counters. Start from the island in the middle. Take turns to flip the coin. Move across the river from island to island.

✓ If the coin lands head up, you can make 1 move.

✓ If the coin lands tail up, make 2 moves.

When you land on a little island with a log on it, collect it to make your dam. Each time you collect a log, mark a log on your dam. You can land on the same island more than once. The first beaver to collect 8 logs to finish his dam is the winner! Rub out the pencil marks to play again.

Ben Beaver's Dam

Squirrels

Red ones and grey ones – what do you know about squirrels?

Nutkin, Tufty and Bushytail – these are all nicknames for one of Great Britain's favourite animals, the squirrel. Let's learn a bit about them – the facts below should help you work out how squirrels got such odd nicknames!

- Squirrels are mammals. They are members of the **rodent** family of animals, which also includes mice and rats.

- There are two kinds of squirrel that live in Britain, the red squirrel and the grey squirrel. The red squirrel is a reddy-brown colour and the grey squirrel is – grey!

- Squirrels are **arboreal** animals, which means that they live mainly in trees.

- Red squirrels have lived in Britain for over a million years.

- Grey squirrels are from America. A few were brought to Britain in 1876 and released, and have been very successful here.

- Squirrels sleep through the coldest parts of the winter. They come out on warmer days to look for food stores they buried in the autumn, especially **nuts** and **acorns**.

- There are about 150,000 red squirrels in Britain, and more than 250,000 grey ones.

- As well as being different colours, squirrels are different in other ways. The grey squirrel is slightly larger and heavier than the red squirrel. The red squirrel has 'tufty' ears and a bushier tail than its grey cousin.

- Squirrels rest and sleep in a ball-shaped nest made of twigs and leaves. It is built in trees and called a **drey**. Squirrels wrap their bushy tails around their bodies like a warm blanket.

- Both types of squirrel use their tails for balancing when climbing trees and fences, and when they jump from branch to branch. Their sharp claws help them cling to tree bark.

- Grey squirrels are quite common, and are found all over Britain. You may have seen them in your garden, or in a park. Red squirrels are harder to find because they live in quiet woodland, and are shy animals. They can be seen in Scotland, Ireland, parts of Wales and on the Isle of Wight.

Photograph: Natural Image

Text: Mike Brennan

The Terrible Twins in...

A Day at the Fire Station

1 The Beaver Colony were going on a visit to a fire station. Brown Beaver told everyone where to meet up. But the twins weren't paying attention.

2 "Where shall I drop you?" said their dad on the day of the visit. "Er ... Green Brigade's Station in North Street," said Luke, hoping for the best!

3 There was a big crowd of people at the fire station. "There they are! Thanks for the lift, Dad," said Jake. "See you later!"

4 The twins couldn't see Brown Beaver. The other people were students, who were taking notes. They didn't take any notice of the twins.

Illustrations: Jon Davis

Text: Sara Peach

28

5 Luke and Jake looked at a big, shiny fire engine while they waited for the others to arrive. They climbed up into the cab and pretended to drive it.

6 The twins nearly jumped out of their skins when the fire bell started to ring. They dived behind the seats and wriggled under a pile of firemen's coats.

7 The firemen slid down the shiny pole and got into the fire engine. They finished getting dressed as the fire engine rushed out of the station.

8 "What's this?" said one of the firemen as he picked up a coat and found Luke hiding under it. "Looks like stowaways," said the fireman who found Jake.

9 "We can explain…" said Luke. But the fireman said, "No time for that now. We're on a 'shout'. You two lads will just have to come along for the ride."

10 The fire engine stopped outside a cottage. "It's my cat," said the lady who lived there. "Look, he's right at the top of the tree! Can you get him down?"

11 The firemen got out a ladder, and in no time at all the cat was safely back down on the ground. "That wasn't very exciting," Luke whispered to Jake.

12 On the way back to the station a message came through on the radio. "Go to Bridge Farm. There's a fire in the hay barn."

13 Green Brigade were soon at the farm. There was smoke billowing from the barn roof. People were leading horses from the stable next door.

14 The firemen used long hoses to spray water on the fire, which was soon out. The twins kept well away. They helped by shooing the chickens to safety.

15 Back on board the fire engine, the chief officer said, "Well done, team. And well done, twins. You were sensible, and you did something useful."

16 The fire engine took the twins to Red Brigade's station, where the rest of the Beavers were waiting. "Those terrible twins!" said Brown Beaver.

17 Brown Beaver looked a bit angry until the twins explained what had happened, and everyone enjoyed the rest of the visit. "Phew!" said Jake and Luke.

Beaver Friends

"Hello! We are all Beaver Scouts from a Colony in Hertford. We love going to Beavers every week because we have lots of fun and meet up with our friends."

Being a Beaver Scout is all about fun and friends!

We have fun making things.

We play games together.

Text: Karen Hankey   Photographs: David Garton

We meet friends from different schools.

We like listening to stories.

We enjoy helping each other.

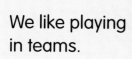

We like playing in teams.

"We are all friends ... because we are all Beavers!"

Arion and the Dolphins

This story from Greece has been told for hundreds of years. Now you can enjoy it!

The king loved music. His favourite singer was called Arion (say it a-ree-on).

One day Arion asked the king if he could go to an island called Sicily. "There's a contest to find the best singer," said Arion. "I want to enter."

The king wasn't sure. "I'll miss you," he said.

"But I might win," said Arion. "Think about the prizes!"

The king thought about the prizes. "Oh, all right then," he said. "Off you go."

Arion sailed off in a big boat.

Arion won the contest. He was a star! He won so many prizes that he couldn't carry them all.

Arion sailed home. But the sailors wanted Arion's prizes. They tried to throw him into the sea.

Text: Brenda Apsley   Illustration: Jeanette Slater

"Let me sing one last song," said Arion. "Please!"

"Go on then," said the sailors.

Arion sang to the gods. He asked them to look after him. Then he jumped into the sea!

Lots and lots of dolphins came to help Arion.

The dolphins took Arion all the way home.

The king was very pleased to see Arion. But he wasn't pleased to see the sailors.

"Arion is staying in Sicily," the sailors told the king. "He didn't win any prizes."

Arion came in. "Oh, yes I did!" he said.

The king sent the sailors away to punish them. Then he asked Arion to sing for him.

"Welcome home," said the king.

"I'm glad to be back," sang Arion.

Beaver Scouts Around the World

Did you know that there are 25 million Scouts all over the world? Many countries have groups for young Scouts, but they are not all called Beaver Scouts, as they are in Britain. Sometimes they have different names.

Let's meet some Beaver Scouts from other countries.

Illustrations: Jeannette Slater

Text: Andy Shepherd

CANADA

Beavers in Canada meet in Colonies.
Promise: I promise to love God and to help take care of the world.
Law: A Beaver has fun, works hard and helps his family and friends.

USA

In the USA, young Scouts are called Tiger Cubs. They have to be seven years old to join. Tiger Cubs usually meet in small groups of between four and eight.
Promise: I promise to love God, my family and my country and to learn about the world.

DENMARK

In Denmark Beaver Scouts are called Micro Scouts. They meet in a Micro Pack of 12 boys and girls, who sometimes share their weekly meetings with older Scouts.

ITALY

In Italy boys and girls can become Castorinos, which is the Italian word for beaver. Groups of about 25 meet each week.

Promise: I promise to be a friend of Jesus, to love everyone and to do everything as well as I can.

AUSTRALIA

In Australia young Scouts are called Joey Scouts. Joeys are young kangaroos, animals that live in Australia. Joey Scouts meet in Mobs for their weekly meetings.

Motto: H O P – help other people.

NEW ZEALAND

In New Zealand young Scouts are called Kea Scouts, the name of a bird found there.

Promise: I will try to share my fun and help others.

Motto: I share, I care, I discover, I grow.

NETHERLANDS

In the Netherlands (also called Holland) Bevers are boys and girls aged between five and seven. At Bevers, they pretend they are visiting Tall-do-all, who wears a big top hat and glasses. Tall-do-all has lots of friends: Pompadom plays music, Quilty makes things and Carrot spends his time in the garden. Everyone dresses up at meetings when doing different things.

Motto: Playing together.

Foxes

Foxes are clever animals that live in cities as well as in the countryside.

Imagine you are out walking in a forest. Out of the corner of your eye, you see a blur of movement. As you turn to look, you see a flash of white disappearing, the tip of a bushy tail. The chances are you have just seen a fox. Let's find out more about these interesting animals.

* Foxes are very successful animals. There are many kinds all over the world. They live in almost every country north of the equator (the line that divides the Earth into two halves).

* The fox that lives in Britain is known as the red fox.

* The fox is a member of the **dog family**. Like all the other members of this animal family, the fox is a muscular, fast-running hunter. It is specially built for finding, chasing and catching prey.

* Foxes are about the size of a small dog. They have pointed ears, thin legs and big bushy tails.

* Male foxes are called **dogs**. Female foxes are called **vixens**. Young foxes are called **cubs**.

* Foxes live underground. Their home is a tunnel with a resting place at the end. It is called an **earth** or **lair**.

* The female fox gives birth to her **cubs** in the spring. The cubs stay underground in the earth until they are between three and four weeks old, feeding on their mother's milk. They spend the next month playing close to the earth, being taught how to hunt and fend for themselves by the mother.

* The fox's tail is sometimes called a **brush**. It usually has a white tip on the end.

* Foxes are **carnivores** (meat eaters). They eat almost anything they can catch, from young rabbits and fish to earthworms and beetles. They also eat wild fruits. In the countryside, foxes are often blamed for killing young lambs and chickens.

* Although most foxes live in the countryside, many have moved to live in towns and even cities, where food is easy to find. They hunt in gardens or rubbish dumps, and often get into dustbins in search of food scraps. They are a good example of an animal that has **adapted**: they have changed how and where they live to survive.

* Have you heard the saying "as cunning as a fox"? It means they are very sly, or crafty. They use their sharp eyesight and hearing to see and hear prey, then sneak up on it and pounce like cats.

* The Latin name for the fox is *Vulpes Vulpes*. An old name that some people still use is **Reynard**.

* You are lucky if you see a fox, because they are very shy animals and only come out very late at night and very early in the morning.

Text: Mike Brennan   Photorpah: Natural Image

Doodle and Scribble in...

The Greedy Little Alien

Text: Mike Brennan   Illustrations: Jo Turner

Many years ago, before you were born, a strange craft from outer space crash landed in Hill Wood near the little town of Lucas End. On board were two alien creatures, Doodle and Scribble. They liked the woods so much they decided to stay on Earth for a while. Since that day they have had many adventures. This is one of them...

The 1st Lucas End Beaver Scout Colony were having their annual picnic in the park. Doodle and Scribble had decided to learn all about humans by secretly watching the Beaver Scouts. This is what they were doing now, from a safe distance, of course.

In the picnic area of the park, the Beaver Scouts were beginning their feast.

"Would you like one of my sandwiches?" Terry asked Julie.

"Yes, please. Would you like some of my orange juice?" replied Julie.

Scribble was amazed by this behaviour and asked Doodle why the Beaver Scouts were giving their food away to each other.

"It's called sharing," explained Doodle. "Sharing is a good thing because it shows that you care about others."

Later, Doodle was preparing a fabulous meal of ant and worm sandwiches for Scribble and himself. As each sandwich was completed, Doodle placed it behind him on the spaceship's kitchen table. When he had finished, he turned around and, to his amazement, saw that all the sandwiches had disappeared!

"Scribble, where are all the sandwiches?" Doodle asked.

"Oh," said Scribble, "I shared them with myself."

The sandwiches had disappeared into Scribble's tummy! He had eaten them all as fast as Doodle could make them. Doodle was not happy.

"That's not sharing," shouted Doodle. "That's called being greedy."

However, Scribble's punishment was not far off. Eating the sandwiches had made him very fat and he was beginning to look and feel a little unwell.

"I feel sick," he said. "I think I'm going to explode."

Doodle had once seen another alien explode and he knew it was not a pretty sight. He decided to look after Scribble and help make him feel better.

Doodle put Scribble to bed and played him some soothing alien music until he went fast asleep.

The next morning, Scribble woke to find he had returned to his normal size and was beginning to feel well again. He had decided he would never, ever be greedy in future.

Just then, Doodle came into the room with an enormous breakfast of worms on toast, fried bugs and a glass of muddy water.

"Here you go," said Doodle. "Now you're feeling better, I though you'd like something to eat."

All of a sudden, Scribble began to feel very queasy.

"Oh, no," said Scribble. "I don't think I can ever eat again. Perhaps you could share my breakfast with the Beaver Scouts. I'm sure they'd like that."

"That's very kind of you, Scribble," said Doodle, "but I don't think they would like it very much."

Well, would you like a breakfast of worms on toast, fried bugs and a glass of muddy water?

Life on Mars

Is there life on Mars?

The planet Mars is our closest neighbour in the solar system – just 480 million kilometres away! The 'red planet' has appeared in lots of science fiction books, comics, television programmes and films. One of the questions that has puzzled man for hundreds of years is, "Is there life on Mars?"

Facts

- Mars is smaller than Earth, and slightly pear-shaped. Its diameter (distance across) is 6,780 kilometres.
- Mars is named after the Roman god of war.
- It takes 687 Earth days to make a Martian year.
- High winds of about 200 kilometres per hour whip up the red dust that covers the planet. This turns the sky reddy-pink and is why Mars is called the 'red planet'.
- Like Earth, Mars has two polar ice caps.
- Mars has two small natural satellites called Deimos and Phobos.
- Mons Olympus is the biggest known volcano in the solar system. It is about 25 kilometres high, which is three times as high as Mount Everest!
- For many years astronomers thought that a network of trenches called Valles Marineris were canals filled with water built by Martians.

Orbiter

1 Lander in aeroshell

2 Entry into Martian atmosphere

Contacts

- Men have been sending probes to Mars since 1962. Mariner 9 was one of the first to orbit the planet.

Rocket braking to touchdown

- In 1971 the Mars 3 Orbiter landed a probe on Mars, but it sent back information for only 20 seconds. Did someone – or something – switch it off?
- The rover vehicle Sojourner landed on Mars on 4th July 1997. It sent back pictures, and collected rock and soil samples. No trace of life was found, though Sojourner is still looking.

Text: Stephen Nixey   Illustrations: Jack Pelling

3 Parachute down to 1,400 m

The biosphere is set up in stages:

Martians

- There could be life on Mars if man decided to live there. Humans could live in big glass 'living bubbles' called biospheres.

- They could grow food plants inside, pumping greenhouse gases into the Martian atmosphere, which would change the sky from pink to blue.
- Temperatures would rise, and the planet would be covered in green plants. Rivers and seas would fill the valleys. If oxygen was pumped out into the atmosphere, humans would be able to leave the biospheres and live on the planet as ... Martians!

45

Have fun and improve your ball skills!

Of all the many sports played around the world, by far the most popular are those played with a ball of some sort. Think about it – football, cricket, tennis, rugby, snooker – all are ball games. Make a list of ball games. How many can you think of?

To become good at any sport you need to practise. Ball games are no exception. Try the following ideas to improve your skills.

Catch

You will need: a tennis ball.

- Stand about 2 metres away from a partner.
- Take careful aim and throw the tennis ball underarm to your partner.
- Your partner must catch the ball using both hands and then throw it back to you.

One Handed Catch

- Play this game like Catch, but this time you and your partner are only allowed to use one hand to catch the ball.
- Remember: you are working together. Throwing well is as important as catching. A well thrown ball is easier to catch.

- As your skills improve, play the game by standing further and further away from your partner. What is the greatest distance apart you can stand and still throw and catch the ball successfully?

Illustrations: Phil Garner

Text: Mike Brennan

Keepy Uppy
You will need: a football.

- Drop the football and allow it to bounce once.
- Using your feet, knees, thighs and head, try to prevent the ball from touching the ground for as long as you can. No hands are allowed!
- Play this game with friends, taking turns to see who can keep the ball off the ground for the longest.
- Try playing the game as a team.
- You can also play this game by throwing the ball into the air and using you head only to keep the ball from touching the ground.
- Your favourite professional footballers often play Keepy Uppy as part of their training.

Bounce
You will need: a basketball or a football.

- Begin by bouncing the ball with one hand. Bounce the ball five times, then bounce the ball in front of yourself across to your other hand and, again, bounce the ball five times. Repeat this routine as many times as you can without losing control of the ball. How many successful switches of hands can you manage?
- Have a competition with your friends to see who can make the most switches.

Double Catch
You will need: two tennis balls.

- Play this game like Catch, but this time you and your partner have a ball each.
- Throw the balls to each other at the same time.
- You can make the game more difficult by clapping before catching the ball.

The ball skills developed in playing Catch can be used in cricket, baseball, rounders and even tennis.

The ball skills developed in playing Bounce can be used in basketball and football (goalkeeping).

Five Monkeys ...

Here are two poems about animals to read out loud.

Five Little Monkeys

Five little monkeys walked along the shore.
  One monkey went sailing,
  So then there were four.

Four little monkeys climbed right up a tree.
  One of them tumbled down,
  So then there were three.

Three little monkeys found a pot of glue.
  Two got stuck in it,
  So then there were two.

Two little monkeys found a big iced bun.
  One ran away with it,
  So then there was one.

One lonely monkey cried all afternoon.
  Then he climbed into an aeroplane,
  And flew off – to the moon!

Illustrations: Phil Garner

48

and an Elephant

The Elephant's Trunk

The elephant carries a great big trunk.
He never packs it with clothes.
It has no lock and it has no key,
But he takes it wherever he goes.

Crafty Things from Cards

Don't throw away old greetings cards – recycle them!

Did you get lots of Christmas and birthday cards this year? Instead of throwing them away, turn them into fun games and puzzles.

Pocket puzzle

❏ Cut a picture from a card into about 6 or 8 'jigsaw' pieces. Can you fit them back together again?

Blindfold path

❏ Stand up two rows of cards about 50cm apart to make a winding path.
❏ Blindfold a friend and see if they can walk along the path without knocking over the cards.

Text: Andy Shepherd   Illustrations: Lindy Norton

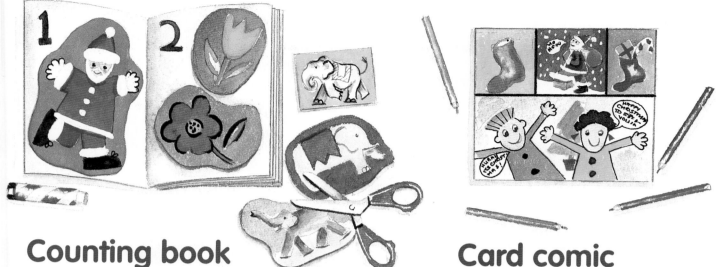

Counting book

Make a counting book for a young child.

❑ Fold 3 sheets of A4 paper in half to make a 'book'. Write Counting Book on the front.
❑ Cut out 1 of something, like a Santa. Glue to the next page and write 1.
❑ Cut out 2 of something. Glue to the next page and write 2. Carry on until you get to 10.

Card comic

❑ Think up your own comic story. Cut out pictures from cards and draw in background scenery and speech bubbles.

Picture snap

❑ Sort out lots of pairs of cards that show the same thing, like robins, snowmen, teddies and Christmas puddings.
❑ Put all the cards face down on a table or the floor.
❑ Play with a friend. Take turns to turn over 2 cards. If you choose 2 the same, you win the cards. The winner is the player with most cards.

Promise puzzle

❑ Choose a large Christmas or birthday card and write the Beaver Scout Promise on the back. Use felt-tip pens in different colours.
❑ Cut the card into lots of little pieces, then try to fit them together again.
❑ Make another puzzle, this time with even more pieces!

Squares, Squares, Squares!

Have some fun with squares and cubes.

The answers are on page 61.

Count the Cubes

The four pictures on this page are drawn in cubes. How many cubes make up each one? Count carefully!

spaceship

dinosaur

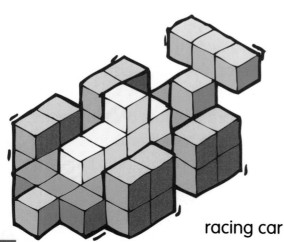

racing car

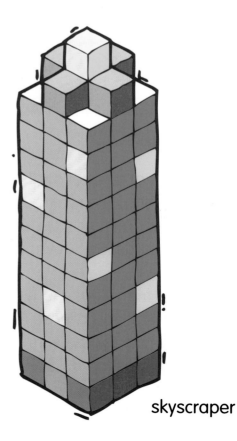

skyscraper

Text: Brenda Apsley   Illustrations: Jeannette Slater

Puzzling Squares

Make a squares picture puzzle.

1 • Cut out a piece of card 12cm x 12cm.

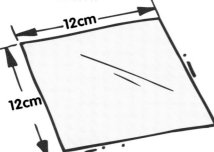

2 • Draw and colour a picture on one side.

3 • On the other side, use a pencil and ruler to divide the card into 3cm squares. Cut them out.

4 • That's the easy part! The difficult part is putting the picture back together again. Can you do it?

• Make a harder puzzle by drawing pictures on both sides of the card.

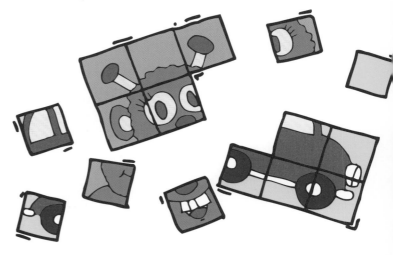

• Make a double-puzzle that's harder still by cutting it into 2cm squares.

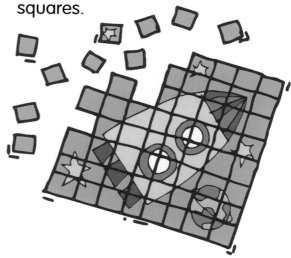

• Make a puzzle that's almost impossible by cutting it into tiny 1cm squares.

Music!

Why not make some simple musical instruments using everyday bits and pieces?

Bottle bells

♪ Collect 8 milk bottles, a metal spoon and a jug of water.

♪ Put the bottles in a row on a table or work top. Pour a different amount of water into each bottle. Start with about 3cm, and add a little more water each time.

♪ Tap each bottle with a spoon. Compare the sound of each one to those on a piano or recorder. With a little practice, you will be able to get a range of 8 notes, **do-ray-me-fa-so-la-te-do!**

♪ Is the note made by the bottle with most water higher or lower than the note made by the first bottle?

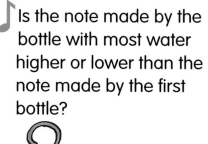

Vibes

♪ Collect a metal coat hanger, a metal spoon, different sizes of large nails and some string.

♪ Tie a row of nails to the coat hanger with pieces of string. Tie the strings close to the hanger, so that the nails do not get tangled.

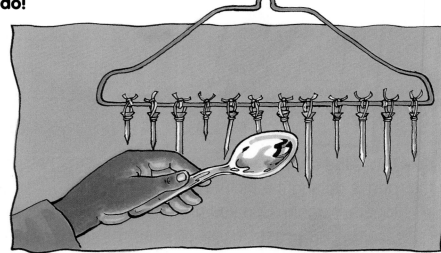

♪ Strike the nails with the spoon. Does each nail make a different sound?

♪ What kind of sound do you make if you run the spoon along the whole row of nails?

Illustrations: Wendy Hesse

Text: Peter Barker

Cymbals

♪ Hold a saucepan lid in each hand and bang together.

Drums

♪ To make deep notes, stretch a piece of cling film over a small bucket or wastepaper bin. Use an elastic band to keep it stretched tight. Bang the drum with your fingertips.

♪ Make smaller drums using jam jars or card kitchen roll tubes. If you use paper instead of cling film does it make a different sound?

Maracas
(shakers from South America)

♪ Fill 2 empty washing-up liquid bottles with dried peas. Hold one in each hand and – shake!

♪ Make different sounds by filling bottles with dried pasta shapes, sugar, sand or rice.

♪ Make smaller shakers using empty tubs with snap-on plastic lids.

A Challenge for Brewster

Brown Beaver had a very special challenge for a Beaver Scout called Brewster.

Brewster was one of the oldest Beaver Scouts in his Colony. One night Brown Beaver asked him if he wanted to try a badge called the Beaver Scout Challenge. It is very special because only older Beavers can do it. She explained that they would do four challenges for the badge, and helped them choose the challenges they wanted to do.

Text: Andy Shepherd   Photographs: Chris Boardman, Andy Shepherd and Dave Wood

Caring challenge

Brown Beaver told them about the Caring challenge. For this, they would choose a Good Turn, which is when you help other people.

Brewster thought about who he would like to help. He remembered old Mrs Smith, who lived next door. He decided that he would help her by doing her shopping every day for a week.

Other Caring challenges could be helping mum or dad, or looking after pets. Or you could plant bulbs or raise money for charity.

Exploring challenge

For the Exploring challenge, the older Beavers had to choose an exciting out-of-doors activity. They decided a trip to the local adventure playground sounded fun.

Other Exploring challenges could be a visit to a theme park, wildlife centre or zoo.

Personal challenge

Next, Brown Beaver asked the Beavers to choose a Personal challenge, something you have never done before.

The others had no trouble thinking up their Personal challenge. Bren decided that he would make his own sandwiches

Scouting challenge

The last challenge was the Scouting challenge, where the Beavers would join in with others in their Scout Group. It could be Cub Scouts, Scouts or Venture Scouts.

The Cub Scouts were going camping, so the Beavers decided to visit them for the day. Akela, the Leader, asked a Cub to show them the tents, then helped them cook their own lunch on the barbecue. The Cubs laid a treasure hunt trail for the Beavers to follow, and the day ended with a sing-song and hot dogs around a camp fire.

It was a great day. Brown Beaver told them that when they were eight, Brewster and the others would be able to swim-up and become Cub Scouts.

for school lunch for a week. He had never done that before! Belinda enjoyed playing football, but she had never scored a goal. She decided to practise hard. Her Personal challenge would be to get a football into the net for the first time!

Brewster remembered that he always had to ask Mum to tie his shoelaces for him. His Personal challenge would be to learn how to tie his laces.

Other Personal challenges could be trying a new sport or hobby, or doing something to look after yourself.

Beaver Scout Challenge

Before long, Brewster finished all his four challenges. One night his parents watched as Brown Beaver presented him with his Beaver Scout Challenge Badge, which he wore on his sweatshirt. She told Brewster that he could do lots more badges in Cubs and put them on his Cub Scout sweatshirt. Brewster couldn't wait!

The Big Book
Competition

**Enter our competition and have fun.
There are great prizes for the lucky winners.**

Imagine a world without books. You wouldn't have books to read for fun, and books to help you find out things. You wouldn't be able to use dictionaries to find the meaning of words – and you wouldn't be reading this annual!

Printed books have been around for about 500 years, and books were first written by hand 5,000 years ago! Even today, when there are lots of other things to do, like going to the cinema, watching telelvision and playing computer games, books are still lots of fun.

Here are some things about books you may not know:

The Beaver Scout Song Book

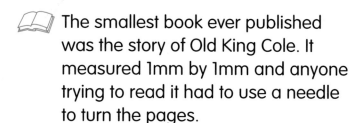

The smallest book ever published was the story of Old King Cole. It measured 1mm by 1mm and anyone trying to read it had to use a needle to turn the pages.

One of the biggest books, called the Super Book, was published in America in 1976. It measured 2.74 metres by 3.07 metres, and weighed more than 250 kilos. It had 300 pages.

Someone borrowed a book from a college library in Cambridge in 1667. It was returned to the library 288 years later. I wonder how much the fine was?

The Bible has been translated into more than 300 different languages.

Competition

If you like books, the Beaver Scout Annual Competition is perfect for you.

There is a great prize for the winner – a big, bumper selection of books. There are prizes for runners-up, too.

Just answer the three questions below. Write your answers, with your name, age and address on a postcard and send it to this address, to arrive no later than 1st February 1999. That's all there is to it!

Send your entry to:

The Big Book Competition
1999 Beaver Scout Annual
The Scout Association
Baden-Powell House
Queen's Gate
London
SW7 5JS

Don't forget to put a stamp on the postcard!

The sender of the first correct entry will be selected at random after the closing date.

• The winner of the first prize will win a selection of books which will include a copy of **The Beaver Scout Song Book**.

• Four runners-up will win a copy of **The Beaver Scout Song Book**.

The questions

Question 3 is not a trick question. It's just for fun, so that we can get an idea of the kind of books you like.

1 What is the name of the bear in **The Jungle Book**?
2 What is the name of the sheep who appears in a story in this annual?
3 What is the name of your favourite book or story?

Prize contents may differ from those shown

And the Winner is...

Adam Rahman

of the 61st Sheffield Beaver Scout Colony!

Congratulations, Adam!

Adam's badge design, shown here, was chosen as the winning entry in the 1998 Beaver Scout Annual Crayola Colouring Competition. Adam's super prize is a bumper pack of Crayola goodies for himself, plus a selection of Crayola goodies to share with his Colony.

The winning design will also be made into a special pin badge for Adam and his Colony to wear.

60

Runners-up prizes have been awarded to:

Demetri Moulinos
of the 25th Warrington East (St Wilfred's Grappenhall) Beaver Scout Colony

and

Simon Brown
of the 35th Croydon Beaver Scout Colony.

Congratulations to Demetri and Simon, whose winning designs are shown below. Both win a selection of Crayola goodies to share with their Colonies.

There was a great response to the competition, and the standard of entries was very high indeed. A big thank you and well done to all the Beaver Scouts who entered.

This year's competition is on page 58.

This is Demetri Moulinos' design, and...

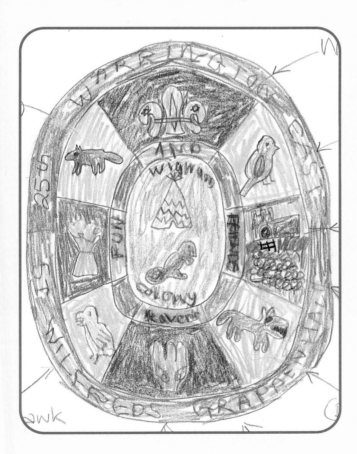

...this is Simon Brown's design.

Answers

Count the Cubes   *page* 52

Dinosaur:	34 cubes
Skyscraper:	105 cubes
Spaceship:	99 cubes
Racing car:	44 cubes